D1592437

BIG BROTHER LEARNS
ALL ABOUT BABIES 1

Itty bitty newborn
(0–3 months)

WRITTEN BY POLLY ZIELONKA

ILLUSTRATED BY MARIA KIRSHINA

Copyright 2020 by Pauline Johnson-Zielonka
All rights reserved.
ISBN: 978-1-7348288-1-8
No part of this book may be used or reproduced in any manner whatsoever
without written permission except in
the case of brief quotations embodied in critical articles and reviews.
Illustrations by Maria Kirshina
© 2020 Pauline Johnson-Zielonka

Dedication

To my two babies: You will not be babies for long.
Watching you grow every day is challenging and amazing,
all at once.

This is Charlie. He just became a big brother to
his baby sister, Emma.
He is learning all about babies.

Baby Emma is very tiny, so Charlie makes sure
to be gentle with her.
He tickles and kisses her toes, and puts on a show for her.

She is not able to hold her toys yet,
but she likes to look at them.

"Shhhh....baby is sleeping."
Charlie quietly watches her as she sleeps.

Baby has lots of growing to do,
which means she needs lots of sleep,
lots of milk, and lots of cuddles.

When baby Emma sleeps, Charlie has quiet playtime
with his mommy and daddy.
They color and do puzzles,
but his favorite thing to do is build with blocks.

WHAAA!!

"Oh no, baby is crying!"

Charlie's mommy explains that babies are not able to talk yet,
so this is Emma's only way of
letting them know when she needs something...

...maybe she needs milk?

...maybe her tummy is bothering her?

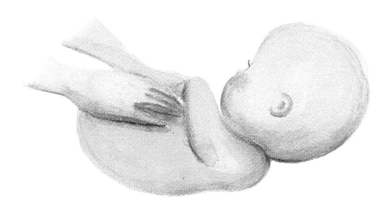

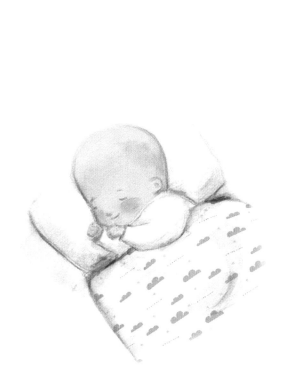

....or maybe it's time for a nap.

Sometimes Charlie helps to calm her down by singing
sweet lullabies.

Baby Emma tries to talk to Charlie.
She coos and makes baby noises.
Charlie lets her know he's listening by cooing back to her.

As baby Emma gets bigger, she smiles when Charlie puts on
a show for her.
She watches everything he does!

Charlie also helps baby with tummy time by putting
toys in front of her.
This helps her get stronger, so she can hold
her head up on her own.
When she gets a little bigger,
she will sit up without any help.

Baby Emma needs to visit the doctor
so they can make sure she's growing well.

The doctor tells Charlie to wash his hands
before he plays with baby Emma.
They have to be careful not to share any germs with her,
so she does not get sick.

Some days Charlie feels frustrated.
It can be hard work being a big brother.
Baby Emma needs a lot of care and attention.

Charlie's mommy says she understands it can be difficult.
She gives him extra cuddles.
Then he snuggles with his
teddy until he feels ready to play again.

Baby Emma's favorite time is when Charlie lays down next to her to read books before bedtime.

But Charlie has to watch out, baby wriggles everywhere! She's still learning how to control her arms and legs.

Charlie gives baby a little kiss on top of her head and says goodnight.

Then he snuggles up for his bedtime!

Made in the USA
Coppell, TX
21 January 2021

48586811R00019